Aesop's Fables for Young Readers

FINISH LINE

A Beka Book® Pensacola, FL 32523-9100
an affiliate of PENSACOLA CHRISTIAN COLLEGE®

Table of Contents

Aesop's Fables
Second Edition

Staff Credits
Editor: Laurel Hicks
Edition Editor: Catherine Pendley
Cover Designer: Michelle Johnson
Illustrator: Stan Shimmin

Cataloging Data
    Aesop's fables for young readers / Laurel Hicks,
  editor; illustrated by Stan Shimmin. — 2nd ed.
    92 p.: coll. ill.; (A Beka Book reading program)
    1. Reading (Primary) 2. Readers (Primary) III. Hicks, Laurel.
IV. Shimmin, Stan. V. A Beka Book, Inc. VI. Aesop's fables.
Library of Congress: PE1119 .A37 1995
Dewey System: 428.4

Word Practice

Read the special sounds and words as quickly as you can.

oo in book

| stood | shook | footing | looking |

ch in church

| reach | chin | chatter | chopper |

a- in asleep

| afraid | along | away | about |

st in stop

| sting | stood | stay | stammer |

Read these long words.

| dinner | little | pretty |
| apple | follow | pillow |

Read the sight words.

have   do   where   said

The Wolf and the Goat

A wolf went out to look for his dinner. Up on a steep cliff stood a little goat.

"I must have that goat," said the wolf. "But how can I reach her?"

"Little goat," said the wolf, "I am afraid that you will fall."

"Do not be afraid," said the goat. "I will not fall."

"But I am afraid. Please come down here. The grass is sweet and fresh."

"I thank you," said the goat. "But I know what you want with me. I will stay where I am. I do not want you to eat me up."

Then the goat shook her horns and ran away. The goat ran far away, and the wolf had no dinner.

Do You Remember?

Circle the words that finish the sentences correctly.

1. The goat stood on a steep _____.

   tower   **cliff**   **ball**

2. The wolf said he was _____.

   hungry   **away**   **afraid**

3. The goat did not want the wolf to _____ her.

   eat   **see**   **pinch**

4. The goat was _____.

   woolly   **big**   **smart**

Word Practice

Read the special sounds. Read the words as fast as you can.

oi in coin	*ou* in out	*fr* in frog
alk in walk	*ir* in bird	*ur* in nurse
ar in stars	*igh* in night	*le* in little

third	loud	turn	fright
hard	walk	surprise	noisy
turtle	garden	thirty	boiling

-ed in wanted	*-ed* in looked	*-ed* in played

point	stop	surprise
pointed	stopped	surprised
mend	walk	boil
mended	walked	boiled

Read and spell the sight words.

again	**friend**	**there**	**oh**
you	**have**	**one**	

The Fox and the Lion

A little fox ran out to play. Just then a lion came along. He made a loud noise.

"Oh, my!" cried the little fox, as he ran away to hide. "That noise is so loud! I shall die of fright!"

Another day the fox ran out to play. Again the lion came along.

"Oh, my!" said the little fox. "Here is the lion again. I wish he would not make that loud noise, but I need not run away."

A third time the little fox ran out to play.

A third time the lion came along.

"Oh, my!" said the little fox. "The lion has come again. I will speak to him."

"Mr. Lion, why do you roar at me?"

The lion was surprised that the fox spoke to him. He was so surprised that he stopped in the middle of his roar. He looked hard at the little fox. Then he walked away.

Do You Remember?

Circle the phrases that finish the sentences correctly.

1. The fox was afraid of the lion's _____.

   loud roar　　　**big feet**　　　**yellow hair**

2. The lion walked away when the fox _____.

   yelled at him　　　**spoke to him**

3. What can you learn from the fox?

The Bible Says: "Be not afraid of sudden fear." —Proverbs 3:25

9

The Wolf and the Crane

One day a wolf was eating his dinner. He ate so fast that a bone stuck in his throat.

"Oh, good friend," he gasped to the crane, "please help me! There is a bone in my throat! With your long bill you can get it out! I will pay you for helping me."

"I will try," said the good crane. So she put her bill down the wolf's throat and pulled out the bone.

"I could have died," said the wolf, as he started to feel better.

"If you will pay me now, I will go," said the crane.

"Pay you! Pay you!" snapped the wolf. "Just be glad that I did not bite off your head!"

Then the wolf trotted off into the wood, thinking that he had played a very smart trick upon the crane.

Do You Remember?

Circle the best answer for each question.

1. Do you think that the crane was a good friend?
   yes   **no**

2. Do you think that the wolf was a good friend?
   yes   **no**

3. Did the wolf keep his promise?
   yes   **no**

4. Which animal would you like to have for your friend?
   the wolf   **the crane**

The Bible Says: "Therefore all things whatsoever ye would that men should do to you, do ye even so to them." —Matthew 7:12

Word Practice

Read these words with suffixes as fast as you can.

doing	tasted	thirsty	fixing
passing	jumped	leaped	sleepy

Circle the little words in these compound words.

into	outside	grandmother
upon	cupcake	daylight
without	handshake	hamburger

Read the sight words.

are	you	doing	Mr.
have	was	there	

The Fox and the Goat

A sly fox fell into a well, and he could not get out.

"What are you doing down there?" asked a goat who was passing by.

"Oh, such good water!" cried the fox. "The best water I ever tasted! Come and have a sip of it."

So down jumped the silly goat. "This is good water," said he. "I was very thirsty."

"Drink all you want," said the fox. And as he said this, he leaped upon the goat's back, then to his horns, then upon the curb of the well, and out upon the ground.

"Good day, Mr. Goat," said he. "I hope you will get all the water you want."

And away he went, leaving the goat to find his way out as best he could.

Do You Know?

Circle the best answer for each question.

1. The fox was very _____.

   playful   **tricky**   **foolish**

2. The goat did not _____.

   drink   **talk**   **think**

3. Did the fox stay to help the goat out of the well?

   yes   **no**

4. Would you like to be a friend of the fox?

   yes   **no**

Word Practice

Read the special sounds and words as fast as you can.

wh in whale	*y* in fly
ch in church	*ir* in bird

while	which	whirl	whisker
why	white	when	wheat

Read these long words.

master	dinner	acorn	napkin
under	ever	secret	mitten

Circle the little words in these compound words.

outside	windmill	teapot
housetop	butterfly	without

Read the sight words.

don't   you   are   said   again

The Dog and the Wolf

One warm day a dog lay down under a tree and was soon fast asleep.

In a little while a wolf trotted out of the woods and was about to eat him up.

"Mr. Wolf," cried the dog, "don't you see how thin I am? I am not fit for you to eat now. Why don't you wait a few days? Then you will find that I will make a better meal. My master is going to have a big dinner next week. Then there will be so much to eat that I shall grow fat."

"Well, if that is true," said the wolf, "I think I will wait a little while. You may go now, and I will eat you after that dinner."

In two weeks the wolf came back, but the dog was not under the tree. He was asleep on the housetop.

"Come down and let me see how fat you are," said the wolf.

The dog awoke and said, "Mr. Wolf, if you ever again see me asleep in the field, you may eat me."

Do You Remember?

Circle the phrase that answers the question correctly.

1. At first, where did the dog take his nap?

    in the field   **on the housetop**

2. What reason did the dog give to the wolf to keep from being eaten?

    he was too fat   **he was too thin**

3. Where did the wolf find the dog the next time?

    in the doghouse   **on the housetop**

4. Why do you think the dog took his nap there?

    to keep from being eaten   **to sleep better**

Word Practice

Read the special sounds and words as fast as you can.

> *ow* in owl   *a-* in asleep
>
> *th* in this   *wh* in whale
>
> *ur* in nurse   *oi* in coin

join	coward	about	either
turn	when	away	ashamed

Read these words with suffixes.

seemed	screamed	shouted	birds
joined	turned	ashamed	beasts

Circle the little words in these compound words.

daylight   indeed   pancake

Read the sight words.

once   don't   you   are   friend

your   again   laughed

The Battle of the Birds and the Beasts

Once the birds and the beasts had a battle.

The bat was a coward and would not take part on either side.

By and by when the beasts seemed about to win the battle, the bat went down and joined them.

"Go away," cried they; "you are a bird."

"Indeed I am not," screamed the bat. "Do you not see my feet and my ears and my fur?"

But soon the battle turned.

The birds seemed about to win
the battle.

Then away went the bat to join
the birds.

"Go away," cried they. "You are
a beast."

"Indeed I am not," screamed the
bat. "Do you not see my wings?"

"You are a coward! You are a
coward! We know your tricks!" And
they drove the bat from the field.

And so ashamed was he, that never again has he come out in the daylight.

Do You Remember?

Circle the best answer for each question or blank.

1. Do we know what the battle was about?

   yes   **no**

2. The bat was not very _____.

   strong   **brave**   **big**

3. Where did the bat go after the birds chased him away?

   to a tree   **to a house**   **to a cave**

Think About It

If you were a beast or a bird, would you want the bat on your side? Why not?

The Lion and the Mouse

A lion lay fast asleep. When he awoke he was hungry. Just then he saw a little mouse in the grass.

In a second the lion had him fast.

"Oh, please don't hurt me!" cried the little mouse. "I am such a little animal. Please don't eat me. Let me go. Some day I may save your life."

"You save my life!" laughed the lion. "What could a little thing like you do for a big lion like me? However, I will let you go. You are too little. I am so hungry that I could eat a hundred mice like you."

Away went the little mouse, happy to be free.

Another day, the lion again was asleep.

Up crept some hunters. Before the lion could wake up and get on his feet, the hunters had bound him with a tight rope.

"Now," said the hunters, "we will go and get our guns and shoot the lion."

The lion growled and roared and kicked, but it did no good.

"Just keep still, my friend," said the little mouse. "I will free you."

"You! Free me!" roared the lion.

The little mouse said nothing but began to bite the rope with his sharp little teeth.

Soon the lion was free. When the hunters came back, they found nothing but a torn rope and a little mouse nibbling at the grass.

Think About It

1. Does it matter to God what size you are?

2. What does God expect you to do, no matter what size you are?

3. Which do you think was braver, the lion or the mouse? Why?

The Bible Says: "But God hath chosen the foolish things of the world to confound the wise; and God hath chosen the weak things of the world to confound the things which are mighty." —1 Corinthians 1:27

Word Practice

Read these long words.

blanket	forest	better	animal
silver	foolish	every	frighten

Read the root words and new words made by adding suffixes.

pass	squeak	mend
passed	squeaked	mended

dress	reach	hate
dressed	reached	hated

Circle the little words in these compound words.

herself	roadside	indeed
anyone	handsome	

Read the sight words.

once   very   many   eyes   there   friends

The Rat and the Elephant

An elephant once passed along the roadside. On his back was a bright red blanket, embroidered with gold and silver. On the blanket sat a king, also dressed in red and gold and silver.

All the animals ran out from the forest to see the elephant pass by.

"Oh, my!" they cried.

"How big!"

"How handsome!"

"What a bright blanket!"

"What a trunk!"

"Pooh!" squeaked a rat, who hated
to hear anyone praised but herself.
"How foolish you are! He can do
nothing but frighten people, even if he
is so big. And I can do as much as
that. Indeed, have I not just as many
legs and eyes and ears as he has?
Besides, I have much softer fur."

But as the rat stood boasting, a cat came creeping up. "Indeed, you are much better in every way than the elephant, my dear rat. At any rate, you are much more to my taste."

And as she spoke, she reached for the rat, and soon there was no rat at all.

"My dear friends," said the cat as she walked away, "you see what comes of boasting and saying bad things about one another."

Do You Remember?

Circle the best answer.

1. How would you best describe the rat?
   wise   **foolish**

2. Whom did the rat like to praise?
   herself   **others**

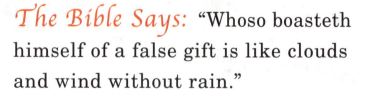

The Bible Says: "Whoso boasteth himself of a false gift is like clouds and wind without rain."

—Proverbs 25:14

Word Practice

Read the words as fast as you can.

catch	snatch	stitch	pitch
latch	crutch	stretch	pitcher

Circle the little words in these compound words.

maybe   cannot   today   beside   into

Read these long words.

rabbit	Peter	catcher	sparkle
fellow	over	turnip	twinkle

Read the sight words.

again   Mr.   very   have   there

The Crow and the Pitcher

Once Mr. Crow had been out in the sun all day long. He was very hot.

"I wish I had a drink," said Mr. Crow. "I have not had a drop of water today."

"Look over to the south," said Peter Rabbit. "Do you see that sand pile? Look beside it. You will find a big pitcher over there. It has water in it. Go and drink all you want."

"Thank you, Peter Rabbit. You are a good fellow," said Mr. Crow.

Off he went to the sand pile. There was the pitcher.

"My mouth is so hot and dry," said Mr. Crow. "Now I shall get a good drink."

But there was just a little bit of water in the pitcher. Mr. Crow put his bill into the pitcher. But he could not reach the water. He tried and tried.

"What can I do?" said Mr. Crow. "I must have a drink."

He stopped to think.

"Maybe I can tip the pitcher over. Then I can get some," said Mr. Crow.

He put his feet on the pitcher. He tried to tip it over. He tried again and again. But he could not tip it over.

"It's too big," he said. "I cannot do it."

Mr. Crow stopped again to think. "Maybe I can put a hole in it," he said.

He pecked it with his bill. He hit it with his wing. He struck it with his feet.

"No," he said. "I cannot do that. I cannot tip the pitcher over, and I cannot put a hole in it."

He stopped again to think. Then he looked at the sand pile.

"Now I know what to do," said Mr. Crow. "I know just what to do!"

He picked up a stone with his bill. He dropped it into the pitcher. The water came up a little. So Mr. Crow picked up another stone. He dropped it in. The water came up a little more. So he put in another stone, and still another. The water came up more and more. At last he could reach it with his bill.

How glad Mr. Crow was! He had found a way at last.

The water was so good. He drank and drank and drank, till he could drink no more.

Do You Know?

1. Why was Mr. Crow so thirsty?

2. Who told Mr. Crow about the pitcher?

3. Why couldn't he get any water from the pitcher?

4. At first, what did Mr. Crow try to do to the pitcher?

5. What was the last thing he did to get water out of the pitcher?

Word Practice

Read the **tch** *and* **wh** *words quickly.*

ditch	batch	when	whinny
crutch	catch	why	whimper

Read the root words and new words made by adding suffixes.

hobble	exclaim	answer	travel
hobbling	exclaiming	answered	traveled

Read these long words.

favor	story	sadly	quickly
different	rather	perhaps	either

Circle the little words in these compound words.

myself	cannot	mailman	inside
anyone	indeed	cupcake	outside

Read the sight words.

were   **your**   **have**   **eyes**

The Blind Man and the Lame Man

A blind man was walking along the road with his cane. Soon he came to a ditch in the road.

Just then a lame man came hobbling along on a crutch.

"Good friend," said the blind man, "will you help me along on this road? I am afraid to go alone."

"I help you!" exclaimed the lame man. "How can I, lame as I am? It is all I can do to get along myself. If I were as strong in the legs as you are, I would ask no favor of anyone."

"Indeed, I am strong in the legs," answered the blind man, "but I cannot see."

"Oh, that makes a different story," answered the lame man. "If you cannot see, it is rather hard for you to get along."

"Indeed it is," answered the blind man sadly.

"Perhaps we can help each other," said the lame man. "You are strong in the legs and I am strong in the eyes. If you will carry me on your back, I will see the way for you."

"I agree," said the blind man. Then away they went, the lame man on the blind man's back.

In this way they traveled very well and reached the end of their trip much more quickly than either could have done alone.

Do You Remember?

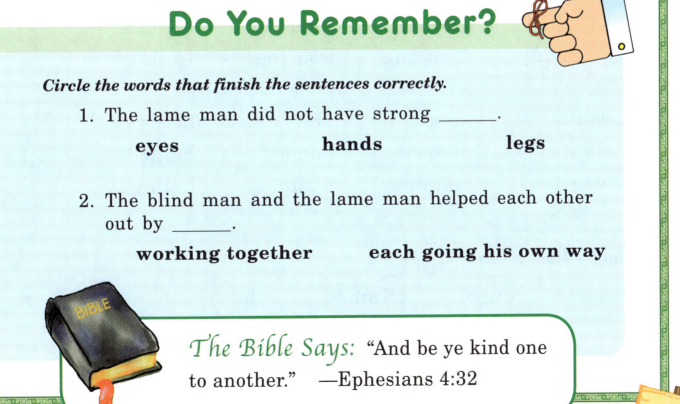

Circle the words that finish the sentences correctly.

1. The lame man did not have strong _____.

   eyes   **hands**   **legs**

2. The blind man and the lame man helped each other out by _____.

   working together   **each going his own way**

The Bible Says: "And be ye kind one to another." —Ephesians 4:32

Word Practice

Read the ear words.

ear in ear

dear	fear	clear	weary	earmuffs
near	year	hear	dreary	gearshift

ear in bear

pear	tear	wear	wears

ear in earth

earn	learn	pearl	search

Read the words.

watch	drop	float	walk
watched	dropped	floated	walked
watching	dropping	floating	walking

want	jump	hop	help
wanted	jumped	hopped	helped
wanting	jumping	hopping	helping

Read the sight words.

one   once   climbed   do

The Bee and the Dove

One day a bee fell into the water. It was a bad fall, for the bee got wet and could not fly out. She could not swim.

A dove watched her fall. "Oh, dear," she said. "I must help that bee."

She took a leaf in her beak, and she dropped it into the water near the bee. The bee climbed up onto the leaf and floated to land.

One day this dove was making a nest. She was flying here and there, getting leaves and hay.

A bad boy looked up at the dove. He picked up a stone to throw at the dove.

As he held the stone, the bee saw him and stung him on the hand. He jumped and dropped the stone, and so he did not hit the dove.

The dove had helped the bee. Now the bee helped the dove.

Do You Know?

1. Why couldn't the bee fly?

2. Who saw the bee? How did she help him?

3. Why was the dove gathering leaves and hay?

4. How did the bee help the dove?

The Bible Says: "They helped every one his neighbor." —Isaiah 41:6

The Wolf and the Dog

Once a wolf met a dog. The dog was fat. He looked as if he had plenty to eat.

The wolf was thin. He looked as if he had nothing to eat.

"You are a lucky dog," said the wolf. "You have plenty to eat. I am half starved."

"Come with me," said the dog. "You shall have what you like to eat."

As they went along, the dog said, "At night I watch the house, and all day I eat or sleep in the yard."

"What is that mark on your neck?" asked the wolf.

"Oh, that is where the chain wears the hair off," said the dog.

"Chain?" said the wolf. "Do you wear a chain?"

"Oh, yes," said the dog. "My master chains me to my kennel all day, but at night I am free to go where I wish."

"Goodbye," said the wolf. "I will not go with you. I may be hungry, but I am free."

Do You Remember?

Circle the best answer.

1. The dog had _____ to eat.

   very little   **nothing**   **plenty**

2. The dog was taking the wolf home to get _____.

   food to eat   **clothes**

Do You Know?

Why did the chain marks on the dog's neck bother the wolf?

The Goose That Laid the Golden Eggs

Once upon a time there was an old lady who had a number of hens, ducks, and geese. She used to send her little girl to the pond every day to take care of the ducks and geese.

But she had one goose that she kept away from the others. This one had a little house and yard of its own.

Why do you think she was so good to this goose?

Each day this goose laid a big, golden egg.

One day the lady sold an egg to pay for a red tablecloth. The next day she got some white earmuffs. Then she got a golden cooking pot and a yellow whisk broom for her kitchen.

The old lady could hardly wait for each new day to come; she wanted that golden egg so much.

At last she said to herself, "I will kill my goose and get all the gold at once."

But when she killed the goose, do you know what she found? Nothing! It was just like all the other geese. She had lost her goose that laid the golden eggs.

The old lady wanted to get rich, but she had become poor.

Do You Know?

1. Why did the lady keep this goose away from the others?

2. Was it wrong for the lady to have this goose?

3. Was it wrong for her to kill it? Why?

The Bible Says: "He that is greedy of gain troubleth his own house."

—Proverbs 15:27

Word Practice

Circle the special sounds. Read the words.

> *ew* in flew   *ew* in few

new	knew	grew	blew	chew
dew	news	jewel	shrewd	crew

Underline the root words and circle the suffixes. Read the words.

camped	asked	flying	wished
watched	barking	cooked	opened

Read these long words.

middle	turtle	hundred	better
between	thousand	sorry	hungry

Read the sight words.

many   **very**   **two**   **Mrs.**

The Proud Turtle

A turtle lived in a brook. All day long he sat on a log. He saw the ducks flying up in the sky. He wanted something new to do. He wished he could fly, too.

Soon some of the ducks came and swam in the brook near the log on which the turtle sat.

"Good ducks, teach me to fly," said he.

"No, we cannot teach you to fly," said the ducks. "You have no wings. You must stay in the brook."

"Yes, you can teach me to fly," said the turtle. "Let two ducks take this stick in their bills. I will hold fast to the middle of it, and you can carry me between you."

So the ducks took the stick in their bills, and the turtle held fast with his mouth.

"Do not open your mouth," said the ducks. "If you do, you will fall to the ground."

"I will not open my mouth," said the turtle.

Away flew the ducks high up into the air. They carried the turtle with them.

As they went over a town, some men looked up at the ducks and the turtle. One of them said, "Who was so wise to think of that?" This made the turtle feel proud. "I was," he said.

But when he opened his mouth to say it, he fell to the ground. And that was the end of the proud turtle.

Do You Know?

1. Why did the turtle want to fly?

2. How did the turtle say he could fly?

3. What did the ducks warn the turtle not to do?

4. Why did the turtle open his mouth?

The Bible Says: "Pride goeth before destruction, and an haughty spirit before a fall." —Proverbs 16:18

The Cat and the Fox

One day when the fox was taking a walk in the forest, he met a cat.

"Do you know any tricks, Mrs. Cat?" asked the fox.

"Oh, yes, I know one or two."

"One or two! Well, that is not many, I must say," said the fox.

"You are right, Mr. Fox. But the tricks I know are very good ones," said the cat. "How many do you know?"

"I know a thousand tricks. I know
a hundred tricks to play on dogs. What
would you do if the dogs came right now?"
asked the fox.

"I would know just one thing to
do."

"Poor Mrs. Cat," said the fox. "I
am sorry for you. Let me teach you
a few of my tricks."

"Listen, Mr. Fox," said the cat. "I
hear dogs barking. There they come!
I will try my one trick now."

As fast as could be, the cat ran
up a tree. The dogs barked at her,
but they could not reach her.

"Now I will see the fox play some of his tricks," said Mrs. Cat.

The fox knew many tricks, but he could not get away from the dogs. They chased him and bit him.

The cat watched from the tree.

"One good plan is better than a hundred tricks," she said.

Do You Know?

1. Why was the cat's one plan better than all the fox's tricks?

2. Why is one good plan better than a hundred tricks?

Word Practice

Circle the special sounds. Read the words.

-er in bigger

faster   stronger   brighter   drummer   helper

-ly in slowly

quickly   nearly   firmly   harshly   softly

old in gold

cold   hold   holding   older   folding

ew in flew

grew   blew   chew   jewel   jewelry

Read the sight words.

you   are   said   only   do   again

The Wind and the Sun

"I am stronger than you are," said the cold north wind.

"Indeed you are not," answered the soft, warm sun.

"Indeed, but I am."

"Indeed, but you are not."

"I will show you that I am stronger."

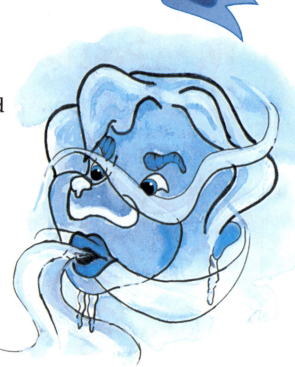

"No, I will show you that I am stronger."

Just then a man came walking along the highway.

"I can get that man's coat off his back," said the cold north wind.

"And I can get that man's coat off his back, too," answered the soft, warm sun.

"Try it," roared the cold north wind.

"You try it first," answered the soft, warm sun.

So the north wind blew a hard, cold blast. The man was nearly blown down. The belt on his coat broke, but he held it close about him and struggled on.

Again the north wind blew. But the man only stood still, holding his coat close until the blast was over.

"It is my turn now," said the sun. So he came out and shone down warmly upon the man.

"First it was cold, and now it is hot," said the man. "I must take off this coat. And here is a cool spot under this tree. I must sit down and rest. I will sleep, and this coat will be my pillow."

What the wind could not do with its harsh blasts, the sun did with its soft, warm rays.

Do You Remember?

1. Why was the north wind unable to make the man take off his coat?

2. Why was the sun able to do it?

The Bible Says: "But the wisdom that is from above is first pure, then peaceable, gentle, and easy to be entreated." —James 3:17

Word Practice

Read the words.

battle	gallop	answer	important
burden	surprise	people	open

Read these words quickly.

-en in sharpen

hard	eat	wood
harden	eaten	wooden

-ly in slowly

sad	quiet	quick
sadly	quietly	quickly

-er in bigger

fold	follow	farm
folder	follower	farmer

-ed in wanted

landed   sounded   tested   waited

The Fly and the Horse

A fly sat on the wheel of a horse cart. "Indeed," cried he, as the strong horses ran along the road, "what a dust I do raise as I go around and around on this big wheel!

"The dust gets in my eyes, too. I will go sit for a while on the horse's harness."

So away flew the proud little fly. After a time he said to the horse, "Now I will fly away. I know I must burden you by resting so long upon your head."

"As you please," snorted the horse. "I did not know you were there until you spoke."

"You did not know I was here!" cried the fly, opening all his eyes in surprise.

"Little people who think they are so important are often mistaken," answered the old war horse.

The little fly's pride was
sadly hurt. He went away
by himself to think about it
all day long, and all the next
day, and all the day after that.

And the horse? Why, he galloped
into battle and soon forgot that a
little fly had ever spoken to him.

Do You Know?

1. Did the fly raise the dust on the wheel as it went
   around? What did?

2. Why didn't the horse know the fly was on his
   head?

3. Why was the little fly's pride hurt?

4. Who do you think was wiser, the fly or the horse?
   Why?

The Bible Says: "For if a man think
himself to be something, when he
is nothing, he deceiveth himself."
—Galatians 6:3

Word Practice

Circle c in city. **Read the words.**

city	mice	race	nice	fence
cent	cell	grace	spice	medicine

Underline the root words and circle the suffixes. **Read the words.**

jumped	helper	golden	burner
going	boiler	fallen	harden

Circle the little words in these compound words.

sunflower	goodbye	birdhouse
something	framework	overcoat

Read the words.

afraid   rather   hungry   visit   happy

Read the sight words.

beautiful   **friend**   **again**

The City Mouse and the Country Mouse

One day a city mouse went to visit a country mouse. The country mouse lived on a farm.

The two mice ran about the farm and had a happy time.

At last the country mouse said, "We must have something to eat." She gave the city mouse an ear of corn.

This tasted good to the country mouse. But the city mouse did not like it.

So she said to the country mouse,
"My friend! Is this all you have to eat?
Come to the city and visit me. I live in
a beautiful house. Come and see what
good things I have to eat."

So the two mice set off for the city.

After a while they came
to the house where the city
mouse lived.

Oh! What good things
the city mouse set before the
country mouse! She had
cheese and cake and sun-
flower seeds.

"How good this is!" said
the country mouse. "I wish
I lived in the city."

Just then a man came into the room. The mice jumped down and ran into a hole.

"Do not be afraid," said the city mouse. "The man cannot see us."

By and by the man went away.

Then the mice ran out of the hole and again began to eat.

Soon a cat came into the room.

"The cat! The cat!" said the city mouse.

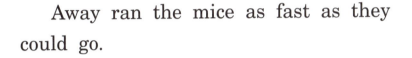

Away ran the mice as fast as they could go.

Poor little country mouse! She said to the city mouse, "Goodbye, my friend. I am going home. In the country I am not afraid. You have a beautiful house and good things to eat. But I would rather be hungry and happy than full and afraid."

The Bible Says: "Better is little with the fear of the Lord than great treasure and trouble therewith." —Proverbs 15:16

The Cat and the Birds

A sly old cat had been told that the birds in the birdhouse were ill.

"I will put on some glasses and an overcoat and visit them," said the cat to himself. "Perhaps they will think I am the doctor. Then if they open their door to me, I will eat them up."

So he crept up to the birdhouse. "I hear you are ill," said he, "so I have come to bring you some medicine."

"Thank you," said the birds, "but we know who you are. We are much more likely to get well without your medicine than with it."

The Bible Says: "Beware of false prophets, which come to you in sheep's clothing, but inwardly they are ravening wolves."

—Matthew 7:15

Word Practice

Circle c in city. **Read the words.**

race   chance   center   circus   parcel

spice   voice   rejoice   Nancy   medicine

Read the words.

turtle   morning   under   bundle

rabbit   river   spider   humble

Underline the root words and circle the suffixes. **Read the words.**

creeping   slowly   reached

creeper   looked   started

Read the sight words.

Mr.   **don't**   **you**   **where**

The Rabbit and the Turtle

One day a turtle was creeping down the road. A rabbit came hopping along.

"Good morning, Mr. Turtle," said the rabbit. "Don't you wish you could run as fast as I can?"

"You run fast and I go slowly," said the turtle. "But I think I can beat you in a race."

"What!" said the rabbit. "You beat me in a race! I can go ten times as fast as you can."

"So you can," said the turtle, "but I may still beat you. Will you run a race with me?"

"Yes," said the rabbit, "but I am foolish to run with an old creeper like you. Where shall we race?"

"Let us go from this big tree to the big tree by the river," said the turtle. "We will start when you count to three."

"One, two, three—go!" said the rabbit.

Away he ran as fast as he could go.

He ran a little way, and then he looked back. The turtle was not in sight.

"I will stop and eat some of these green leaves," said the rabbit. "Then I will run on to the tree."

So he stopped and ate the green leaves. Then he said, "That old creeper is not in sight. I will lie down awhile and rest. Then I will run to the big tree by the river. I shall be there long before Mr. Turtle comes."

So the rabbit lay down, and soon he was fast asleep.

When he woke up, he looked back.
He did not see the turtle.

"I may as well go on," he said.

He ran to the big tree by the river.
There under the tree sat the turtle!

The turtle was slow, but he did not
stop until he had reached the end of the
race. And that is how he won.

Do You Know?

1. Why did the turtle ask the rabbit to race him?

2. Why did the rabbit think himself foolish to race?

3. The rabbit could have won the race. Why didn't he?

The Bible Says: "Let us run
with patience the race that is
set before us." —Hebrews 12:1

Word Practice

Circle ea **in thread.** *Read the words.*

bread   spread   breath   ready

head   feather   heaven   weather

Read the words.

-*y* in rainy

thirst   dust   greed   might   health

thirsty   dusty   greedy   mighty   healthy

-*ed* in looked

jumped   talked   winked   wished   pumped

washed   walked   stamped   crushed   watched

-*ed* in played

growled   rubbed   called   steamed   churned

-*ly* in slowly

softly   hardly   freely   rapidly   heavenly

Read the sight words.

laughed   anything   very   together

again   one   of

The Fox and the Grapes

It was a very warm day. "I am so hungry and so thirsty," said the fox, as he came along the dusty road.

"Oh, there are some fine grapes! What luck! I will have those grapes." So he gave one big leap up to the vines, but he could not quite reach them.

Again he jumped, and again and again. But each time he fell back more and more out of breath.

Then he sat and looked at them.

"Sour old things!" he growled. "I would not eat one of them. They are not good for a fox. I will leave them for the greedy birds. Birds will eat anything."

Then he went away; and the grapes rubbed their soft cheeks together and laughed softly at the silly old fox.

Do You Know?

1. Why did the fox want the grapes?

2. Did the fox know for sure the grapes were sour?

3. Why did he say the grapes were sour?

The Bible Says: "The tongue of the wise useth knowledge aright: but the mouth of fools poureth out foolishness." —Proverbs 15:2

"I know why the swan is so white," said the jet-black raven. "He swims in the water all the time. I will go and swim in the water. Then I shall be as white as he."

So the raven flew up and down the land until he found a lake of clear, cool water.

"Here I will make my home," said the raven, "and every day I will swim in the water."

So the raven made his home by the lake, and every day he swam in the water.

But he got a bad cold from being so much in the water, and he very nearly lost his voice.

"Croak, croak," said he, "I shall go back to the ravens. My feathers are much better looking than any swan's feathers. I would not trade their color for all the world. Croak, croak!" and away he flew.

Think About It

1. Did the lake help the raven get white feathers? Why?

2. When the raven left the lake, was he really happy with his feathers? Why?

3. Who wants us to be happy with the way He made us?

The Bible Says: "And be content with such things as ye have."
—Hebrews 13:5

Word Practice

Circle the special sounds. Read the words.

ie in brownie

cookie   piece   yield   believe   field

aw in saw

caw   law   draw   straw   dawn

jaw   lawn   drawl   fawn   hawk

ear in ear

dear   near   nearly   weary   disappear

ea in thread

feather   head   leather   bread   meadow

Read the words.

suppose   flatter   began   feathers   forest

Read the sight words.

Mrs.   **laughed**   **beautiful**   **are**

were   **eyes**   **your**

The Fox and the Crow

A crow stole a piece of cheese and flew up into the tree with it.

As she sat there on the branch, a fox came running along.

"Oh, that cheese!" said he. "How good it smells! How I would like it!"

He came close up under the tree and said, "Dear Mrs. Crow, how beautiful you are. I did not know you were so beautiful! How bright your eyes are! And how your feathers shine in the sunlight!"

The silly old crow was flattered and began to rub her feathers.

"I suppose you can sing," continued the fox. "I know you can! You must have the sweetest voice in all the forest. Please sing one note for me!"

"Caw! caw!" cried the crow.

"Ha, ha!" laughed the fox, as the cheese dropped from her bill. "Your voice is very good, and so is the cheese."

Do You Know?

1. How did the crow get the piece of cheese?

2. Why did the fox speak so sweetly to the crow?

3. Do you think the fox meant what he said? Why?

The Bible Says: "Meddle not with him that flattereth with his lips."
—Proverbs 20:19

Word Practice

Circle the special sounds. Read the words.

(*ea* in steak)

break	yea	great	greater	greatly

(*ie* in brownie)

piece	field	niece	shriek	chief

(*old* in gold)

bold	cold	scold	golden	behold

(*wor* in worms)

worms	word	work	worth	world

Read the words.

worked	greedy	chirped	called	answered

Read the sight words.

one	very	where	busy
any	there	to	you

The Rooster and the Piece of Gold

"Come along," said the rooster to the hens one morning. "I am very hungry and so are you. Let us go to breakfast."

"Cluck, cluck! where shall we go?" said the hens.

"Over in the garden are some fat worms and bugs."

So away they all ran to get the worms.

"Cluck, cluck!" cried the old mother hen. "See what I found."

"Cluck, cluck! cluck, cluck!" cried the other hens, running to see.

"Cock-a-doodle-doo-oo!" called the old rooster as he went to look.

"Cluck, cluck! how it shines!" said the mother hen.

"It is a piece of gold! a piece of gold!" cried the other hens.

"So it is," said the rooster, "but it is of no use to us. I'd rather find a fat worm when I'm hungry than a whole bag of gold."

Think About It

1. What were the rooster and the hens looking for?

2. What did one of the hens find?

3. Was the gold of any use to them?

4. Do you think the rooster was wise or foolish? Why?

The Ants and the Lazy Grasshoppers

In a great field lived the ants and the grasshoppers. The ants were busy little people. They worked all summer getting grain for the winter.

"We shall need it to eat," said the wise ants.

"I'd rather hop in the sun!" said a grasshopper.

"But there will be snow in the winter. Then we can get no food!" answered the ants.

"But the sun is so nice and warm!" chirped the grasshoppers.

By and by winter came. Oh, how cold it was! The grasshoppers' legs were stiff with cold. And they were so hungry.

"Please give us some grain, dear ants," begged the grasshoppers.

"We do not have any extra," answered the ants.

"But we have none at all!" cried the grasshoppers.

"What were you doing all summer?" asked the ants. "Why did you not store away some grain then?"

"Oh, we could not! We danced and hopped and sang all summer long!"

"Then why not dance and hop and sing all winter, too?" answered the ants.

"How greedy ants are!" chirped the lazy grasshoppers.

"How lazy grasshoppers are!" thought the busy ants.

Do You Know?

1. Why didn't the ants want to play all summer?

2. Why did the grasshoppers want to play all summer?

3. Do you feel the grasshoppers were fair in calling the ants "greedy"? Why?

4. Do you feel the ants were fair to call the grasshoppers "lazy"? Why?

The Bible Says: "Go to the ant, thou sluggard; consider her ways, and be wise." —Proverbs 6:6

The Fox and the Crab

A little crab said to his mother, "I would like to go across the field up to that shining sand."

"Your place is here in the water," snapped the mother crab.

"But it looks so pleasant up there in the sun!" pleaded the little crab.

"A fox will catch you if you go on land," snapped the mother again.

"But I want to go," sulked the little crab, and off he went.

How nice and warm it was! How the sand shone in the sunlight!

"Oho!" said a fox coming along just then. "Here is my breakfast all ready for me!"

Crack! crack! went the crab's thin shell. Soon there was no crab at all.

But there was a fox with a nice breakfast just eaten.

The Bible Says: "Honor thy father and thy mother: that thy days may be long upon the land which the Lord thy God giveth thee."

—Exodus 20:12

Word Practice

Circle the special sounds. Read the words.

aught in caught

taught   daughter   haughty   naughty

ear in ear

clear   year   near   nearly   nearby

c in city

rice   race   grace   graceful   gracefully

ea in thread

head   spread   dread   leather   weather

ear in earth

earn   learn   pearl   heard   search

Read the sight words.

beautiful   have   been

One hot day, a stag came to a lake to drink.

The water was so clear that he could see himself in it.

"Oh, what beautiful antlers I have!" he cried. "How strong and how graceful they are! And they spread out like the branches of a tree! But what homely legs I have! So long and so thin!"

Just then the stag heard the horn of the hunters.

Away flew the stag. How swiftly his long legs carried him!

But the beautiful antlers caught in a tree. And before he could get them free, the hunters caught up with him.

"These miserable antlers!" cried he, as the hunters shot him. "I was so proud of them, but they have been the death of me."

Do You Remember?

1. Why did the stag admire his antlers?

2. Why did he dislike his legs?

3. How did the antlers hurt him?

The Bible Says: "Pride goeth before destruction." —Proverbs 16:18